We Are Gems

Healing from Anti-Asian Microaggressions through Self-love & Solidarity

Written by Ko Kim
Illustrated by Christine Yoon
and
Andrew Hem

To: Chloe ♥
You are a precious
gem. Shine!
Ko Kim

Dedicated to all our grandmothers

We are gems,
shimmering with wisdom
handed down from our Asian and Asian American elders.

You may face cuts and scrapes called microaggressions. But like those before you, your inner luster will blaze if placed in shared liberation.

3

Shared liberation is solidarity with our Black and Indigenous neighbors against systemic racism—laws, traditions, and behaviors that harm people with African and Indigenous roots from classrooms to courtrooms.

Only through solidarity will we glisten.

4

So when people ask you, "Where are you *really* from?" reply that you are at home as long as you hold sacred the air, water, soil, animals, and plants. Reply that you are at home when you honor Indigenous elders.

Then ask in return, "How are we taking care of all that has life? When Indigenous youth and elders resist polluting pipes, how do we respond?"

Our liberation is bound to the life and dignity of Indigenous Peoples.

When they advise you to, "Speak up," tell them to listen closely. Our voices have been roaring for generations. Then ask, "How intently do you listen to the hopes and dreams of Black activist leaders? For seven decades, Grace Lee Boggs rallied for fair wages and housing alongside Black community organizers. Ram Manohar Lohia introduced civil disobedience to the Highlander Folk School, helping Rosa Parks and Martin Luther King, Jr., prepare for the fight for freedom."

Our liberation is tied to Black joy.

When they ask you, "How could you be Asian? Your eyes aren't slanted," or, "Can you see with those slanted eyes?" tell them that whatever their shape, your eyes can clearly see the housing, schooling, policing, and banking policies that pit communities against one another.

Then ask, "Can you follow the thread that knots our segregated lives to the laws that harm Black Americans and erase Indigenous Peoples?"

Our liberation is creating and upholding just laws.

When people try to compliment you with, "You speak English so well," remember that you and so many of your neighbors are anchored in multiple cultures.

Then ask, "Do you know that this land is beaming with 169 Indigenous languages? That our cosmos is glittering with 6,500 languages, each millennia upon millennia old? Do you know that I love and live in many worlds?"

Our liberation is universal.

When people try to commend you with, "You are unlike *the others*," reply that you are not straining yourself toward the dull cast of sameness.

Then tell them, "I am blooming as myself under the light of the Divine and the glow of our grandmothers."

13

Our liberation is self-love.

14

When they pick apart your traditions and claim, "I know all about that," say that you are delighting in the inheritance of your ancestors.

Then ask, "Who were your great, great grandparents? Which shorelines sunk into the horizon on their way to here? What were the customs, religions, foods, and languages of those lands?" In that moment, as they ache to remember, ask, "What did you trade to not know?"

Our liberation is the history in our veins.

When people try to dim your glow with, "_____," (because microaggressions are ever-changing), tell them that we already labored *and* protested under the weight of those crops, enlisted for *and* objected to those wars, and survived *and* rebelled in those camps.

Tell them that we are stepping away from the Ladder for we are gems, radiating with this wisdom from our elders:

Our liberation is inclusive, bound to the liberation of all.

Author's Note

A friend's daughter came home from school, sobbing. A racial microaggression had been lobbed at her in class. It stung to see my scars as fresh cuts on a child. So I wrote this book for my adopted niece and the wounded child in many of us.

This book is just one story, not *the* story, about racial microaggressions and Asian Americans. I recognize that the label Asian American covers 19+ ethnic groups. My hope, then, is that this book highlights shared experiences among different Asian American identities and unites us in the fight for racial justice and healing. In this way, I hope to honor the work of our elders Emma Gee and Yuji Ichioka, who coined the term Asian American in 1968 to create a political—not ethnic—identity to resist hate.

My ultimate hope is that readers are reminded that anti-Asian microaggressions are neither isolated nor innocent. Rather, these microaggressions (along with anti-Arab, anti-Latinx, and anti-Pacific Islander racism) are offshoots of our country's old and ever-evolving oppression of Black Americans and Indigenous Peoples in the name of progress and profit. And so, in learning to love myself and all my neighbors, I must address the anti-Black and anti-Indigenous racism within myself, my family, community, and institutions. Entwined, we will wither or flourish together.

More background information for young people, caregivers, and educators

Microaggressions [*noun*]: Subtle comments or behaviors—intentional or unintentional—that belittle and hurt a person because of their background and identity. Sometimes, the person on the receiving end of a microaggression may feel confused about the experience and question their hurt feelings, because the microaggression was delivered as a supposed compliment, joke, or advice. (This definition is based on the works of Derald Wing Sue, a professor of counseling psychology at Columbia University. The term was first coined by Harvard professor and psychiatrist Chester M. Pierce in 1970.)

Microaggression #1: "Where are you really from?"

This seemingly innocent question is harmful because it assumes that only people of European heritage or White people belong in the United States.[1] *But this land has always been home to millions of Indigenous Peoples—15,000 years and counting.* Additionally, this microaggression overlooks and dismisses ten generations of Asian Americans (e.g., Filipino settlements in present-day Louisiana, circa 1763).

This brings us to an uncomfortable truth: like those of European descent in this country, many Asian Americans are participants of **settler colonialism.** What does this mean? Many of us Asian Americans are using resources and settling lands that were taken from Indigenous Peoples. What can we—settlers of Asian descent—do to lessen this harm? A few possible starting points:

- Acknowledge that settler colonialism has been ongoing in the Americas since 1492

- Look into whose Indigenous land one is living on (search: "Native land maps") and respectfully work to understand that Tribal Nation's concerns and dreams

- Be in solidarity with today's Indigenous-led movements through votes, other forms of civic engagement, and donations (#waterislife #nodapl #mmiwg2s #defundline3).

[1] This text adopts Eve Ewing's stance on capitalizing the "W" in writing about White people and Whiteness. The term Whiteness describes a position of power (not a feeling of power) that European descendants hold in our country's false racial hierarchy. Capitalizing the "W" for both terms is neither an elevation nor a degradation of any individual or group. This approach is rather meant to love and encourage our White neighbors to pursue racial justice not only for others but also for themselves because Whiteness comes at a cost even to people of European descent. For more information on the cost of Whiteness, please check out this online learning portal by the National Museum of African American History and Culture: https://nmaahc.si.edu/learn/talking-about-race/topics/whiteness

Microaggression #2: "Speak up."

Many Asian Americans *do* speak up. During the World War II internment of Japanese Americans, there were protests across all ten camps. Our elder Fred T. Korematsu refused to be interned, appealing his case all the way to the Supreme Court with help from the American Civil Liberties Union (*Korematsu v. United States, 1944*).

Other Asian American elders of justice include—but are not limited to—Al Robles, Bill Sorro, Emil De Guzman, Estella Habal, Jagjit "J.J." Singh, Kiyoshi Kuromiya, Larry Itliong, and Yuri Kochiyama. Each leader is known for their cross-racial and/ or intra-racial solidarity:

- **Al Robles, Bill Sorro, Emil De Guzman,** and **Estella Habal** helped to organize Chinese American and Filipino American tenants of the International Hotel in San Francisco. They led a ten-year eviction strike with support from activists of all backgrounds.

- **Jagjit "J.J." Singh** founded the India League of America. In collaboration with Filipino American organizers, Singh successfully advocated for the Luce-Celler Act of 1946, which allowed Filipino and Indian residents to become U.S. citizens.

- **Kiyoshi Kuromiya** worked with Martin Luther King, Jr., and marched in the South during the spring and summer of 1965. He later became a prominent advocate for gay rights (LGBTQIA+).

- **Larry Itliong** reached out to Dolores Huerta and César Chávez to create a labor coalition between Filipino American and Mexican American farm workers in 1965. This led to the success of the Delano Grape Strike (1965-1970). Yemeni American farm workers also played a key role in this labor movement, refusing to cross the picket line.

- **Yuri Kochiyama** collaborated with Black community leaders, including Malcolm X, to fight for human rights. She later organized protests against the Vietnam War and helped to pass the Civil Liberties Act of 1988, winning reparations for Japanese American internment survivors.

Today, Asian Americans continue to make noise. There are activists like:

- Ai-jen Poo
- Alok Vaid-Menon
- Cha Vang
- Kim Tran

- Michelle Kim (no relation)
- Rinku Sen
- Thenmozhi Soundararajan
- Valarie Kaur

Additionally, there are advocacy groups like:

- Asian Americans Advancing Justice
- Asian American Advocacy Fund
- Desis for Progress

- Equality Labs
- Kabataan Alliance
- Southeast Asia Resource Action Center

In short, this microaggression to "speak up" is based on a stereotype that Asians and Asian Americans are meek and quiet (and economically successful). Let us call this stereotype by name so it loses its harmful hold on us: the **Model Minority Myth**.

The Model Minority Myth is most disastrous because it pits Asian Americans against Black Americans. Sadly, some argue that because Asian Americans *seem* to be doing well, all non-White peoples, especially Black Americans, should be doing just as well. However, this argument misses two facts:

1. The label Asian American represents over 19 ethnic groups with starkly varying levels of income and wealth.

2. The systemic oppression that many Black Americans face—e.g., intergenerational trauma from 246 years of chattel slavery, 103 years of Jim Crow laws backed by lynchings, and 50+ *ongoing* years of mass incarceration and overpolicing—differs from the oppression that many Asian Americans face. (This point is made not to rank or invalidate anyone's or any group's racial trauma; rather, it is to show that *different kinds of historical oppression exist*, and each requires tailored solutions and solidarity.)

In short, the Model Minority Myth paints over the struggles of Asian Americans, especially Southeast Asian Americans, in order to justify ongoing racism toward our Black neighbors.[2] *Thankfully, there are many Asian Americans speaking up and challenging this toxic myth, refusing to be instruments for anti-Black racism. We are aware that* **Black Americans and Asian Americans are staring down different heads of the same White supremacy hydra.**[3]

---

[2] The Model Minority Myth particularly erases the struggles *and* strengths of Southeast Asian Americans—many who are survivors/ refugees from Cambodia, Laos, and Vietnam (including Hmong and Mien families). According to a 2020 report by the Southeast Asia Resource Action Center and Asian Americans Advancing Justice - Los Angeles, over one million Southeast Asian Americans are living in low income households while 460,000 are living in poverty. (https://www.nbcnews.com/news/asian-america/largest-u-s-refugee-group-struggling-poverty-45-years-after-n1150031)

[3] Sadly, White supremacy—or the false belief in the superiority of White people—helped to bring about the Chinese Exclusion Act of 1882 and the 1930 Watsonville Riot against Filipino Americans. More recently, many Asian Americans have been traumatized by hate speech, physical violence, and the loss of business due to COVID-19 scapegoating. Meanwhile, many of our Black neighbors have been dealing with unjust criminalization (#joggingwhileBlack #sleepingwhileBlack), inequitable access to healthcare, and voter suppression—all tied to White supremacy *and* extractive economics. Given White supremacy's many forms across different groups, cross-racial solidarity seems necessary. (It is worth noting that countless Black Americans have been fighting White supremacy since 1619. For more on Black resistance and resilience, please check out *Stamped from the Beginning: The Definitive History of Racist Ideas in America* by Ibram X. Kendi.)

Microaggression #3 and #4: "How could you be Asian? Your eyes aren't slanted," or, "Can you see with those slanted eyes?"

Why are such questions (sometimes) asked by strangers and coworkers with sincerity? One possible answer: centuries of disconnected lives *by design*.

Economist Richard Rothstein shows that federal housing and banking policies, along with local city ordinances, divided neighborhoods by race throughout the U.S. (even after the Civil Rights Movement of the 1960s). As a result, many of us grew up—or are growing up—in racially segregated communities with few opportunities to learn from and about different cultures. And so such hurtful questions linger.

For more details about *de jure* (by law) segregation in housing, please see:

- *The Color of Law: A Forgotten History of How Our Government Segregated America* by Richard Rothstein[4]

- "The Case for Reparations" by Ta-Nehisi Coates (*The Atlantic*). Coates centers the voices of Black families directly impacted by **redlining** (the Federal Housing Administration refusing to insure mortgages in Black neighborhoods) and **restrictive covenants** (home deeds forbidding the sale of property to anyone who is not White). Sadly, redlining and restrictive covenants blocked Black homebuyers from receiving fair loans and purchasing property from Los Angeles to New York (1930s-1970s).

[4] Rothstein argues for racial integration. *And* unfortunately, integration has come to mean over the years: a small number of Black families adjusting to a mostly White neighborhood and culture. Laws and practices that support true integration (i.e., honors Black families) must center real input from our Black neighbors and scholars.

Microaggression #5: "You speak English so well."

Ronald Takaki breaks down this microaggression in *A Different Mirror: A History of Multicultural America.*[5] He observes that many Asian Americans (though born in the U.S.) are often seen as foreigners and not fluent in English. Meanwhile, descendants of European settlers are automatically viewed as Americans and "native" English speakers. Takaki argues that our country's popular but false origin story—that White settlers founded the U.S. on "empty" and "free" land (rather than land taken from Tribal Nations through organized warfare and genocide)—creates this double standard.

In addition, this microaggression erases the existence of Indigenous Peoples (574 Tribal Nations) and their languages (169+ languages), assuming English is the only language of these lands.

[5] Takaki writes about experiencing this microaggression nearly 100 years *after* his ancestors first settled in the U.S.

Microaggression #6: "You are unlike the others."

This microaggression is based on the harmful assumption that non-White peoples should strive to emulate White culture as much as possible. This is why, sadly, some Asian Americans try to claim Whiteness and/ or distance themselves from their Black neighbors by buying into the Model Minority Myth.[6]

Many of our Asian American elders, such as Grace Lee Boggs and Larry Itliong, realized that such distancing only reinforces oppression and harms everyone.[7] For this reason, they dedicated their lives to cross-racial solidarity. Today, we can continue the work of our elders by honoring and valuing Black and Indigenous lives.

[6] True, the idea of race is completely made up. However, race and racism continue to deeply influence our lives. As Toni Morrison once pointed out in an interview, "Race is a construct; a social construct. And it has benefits. Money can be made off of it. People who don't like themselves can feel better because of it. It can describe certain kinds of behavior that are wrong or misleading. So [race] has a social function."

[7] This includes distancing oneself *from* oneself—or growing estranged from one's cultural heritage in assimilating to Whiteness. Distancing also includes viewing fellow members of the same identity group as competitors or threats.

Microaggression #7: "I know all about that."

Well-meaning, non-Korean acquaintances tell me that they "know all about" my culinary heritage—as though 5,000 years of Korean history could be distilled from a food vlog. How can we explain such overconfidence? The answer is a **colonial mentality** resulting from European and Anglo-American colonialism.[8]

A colonial mentality views non-European cultures as simple and/ or inferior. More notably, it views non-Western languages, religions, clothing, customs, and cuisines as hobbies to be mastered or knowledge to be accumulated (rather than foundational and sacred parts of another person's identity).

This dismissive mentality goes beyond microaggressions. It explains, for example, why we have more children's books written by White authors than Black, Indigenous, Latinx, Pacific Islander, and Asian writers, *combined.*[9] It also explains why some government agencies, nonprofits, or school districts—though lacking robust Black and Indigenous community input and/ or board membership—assume to know what is best for Black and Indigenous communities.

For more information on colonialism and its impact on our minds, hearts, bodies, and institutions, please see:

- *An Indigenous Peoples' History of the United States* by Roxanne Dunbar-Ortiz

- *My Grandmother's Hands: Racialized Trauma and the Pathway to Mending Our Hearts and Bodies* by **Resmaa Menakem**

[8] Colonialism is when an outside nation takes control of the land, resources, labor, and culture of another nation for profit. This profiteering process occurs when the invading country: 1.) views the Native peoples as less-than, 2.) sends settlers with supposed "superior" culture to occupy the land, and 3.) uses or threatens to use brutal force. Of course, European countries are not the only nations to have engaged in colonialism. However, European colonialism stands out for its global reach and run. According to historian Marc Ferro, over 100 nations survived British, Dutch, French, Portuguese, and Spanish occupation in the past millennium (*Colonization: A Global History*). The British Empire alone occupied *62+ present-day countries, including large tracts of land that would later become part of the United States.* Our country's racial hierarchy—however false—and colonial mentality are the direct result of European and Anglo-American colonialism.

[9] http://ccblogc.blogspot.com/2020/06/the-numbers-are-in-2019-ccbc-diversity.html

Thank you to our Kickstarter Backers!

Abbie Korman
Alejandra Flores
Alvaro Loza
Alysa McCall
Amy Gonzales
Andrew Kupasrimonkol
Ann & Larry Wright
Anonymous
Ara Ko
Arianna Craig Vazquez
Ashly Ball
Ben & Tina Brenner
Caila Parodi
The Calderón Family
Cate Taylor
Chloe Liang
Chris Yoon
Christine Yang
christy mcguire
Edwin Hong
Edwin Ushiro
Erica Hooton
Erin Brannan
Elizabeth Hubbard
Ellis

Holly Tan
Ivy Paek
Lunas4Kindness
James Thivierge
Jane Kim
Jane Lee
Jasmine Paul
Jennie Cochran-Chinn
Jenny Chu
Jenny Jew
Jenny Tran
Jessica Cuevas
Jessica Yum
Karen Lee
Katherine McDougall
Katherine Wright
Kathryn Rice
Kirby Patterson
Kori Maughmer & John Elliott
Kristen Melelani Walker
Laura Lai
Lauren Kang
Lehmann Sio
Lena Potts
Lina Swislocki

Linda Phuong Nguyen
Manuel Celedon
Melissa Kim
Nicole Taylor
Pati Romero
Robert Abad
Ryan & Erin Wright
Samantha Kanagaraj
Samantha Sundquist
Sammy Park
Sandy Myint
Sarah-Mei Estrada
Sarah Dane Lara
Shenne Hahn
Silvia Romero
Stephanie Lee
Tamara Setiady
Taryn West
Tess & Renil Zachariah
Tiên Le
Viroqua & Phaedra
Yuka Walton
Yumi Lawlor

A special thank you to Michael Kim-Eubanks, Stacey Parshall Jensen, and Ryan Wright for their suggestions and insights. A deep thank you to the Native Governance Center's Style Guide on decolonizing language.

CPSIA information can be obtained
at www.ICGtesting.com
Printed in the USA
BVHW092131291222
655269BV00001B/4

9780578285566